Doc is the Wiz.
He has on a big hat.

Doc taps the mop.
Zot!
The mop is a doll!

Doc taps the doll.
Zot!
The doll is a top.

3

Doc taps the top.
Zot!
The top is a box.

Doc taps the box.
Zot!
The box is a dog.
The dog has lots of dots.

5

Doc taps the dog.
Zot!
The dog is a pot.
The pot is hot!

Doc taps the pot.
Zot!
Lots of fog pops out of the pot.

Doc taps the fog.
Zot!
The fog got Doc!